GREEK STREET
CASSANDRA COMPLEX

GREEK STREET

CASSANDRA COMPLEX

PETER **MILLIGAN**
WRITER

DAVIDE **GIANFELICE**
ARTIST

PATRICIA **MULVIHILL**
COLORIST

CLEM **ROBINS**
LETTERER

DAVIDE **FURNO**
ORIGINAL SERIES COVERS

GREEK STREET
CREATED BY PETER MILLIGAN
AND DAVIDE GIANFELICE

KAREN BERGER SVP – Executive Editor WILL DENNIS Editor – Original Series
MARK DOYLE Associate Editor – Original Series BOB HARRAS Group Editor – Collected Editions
SCOTT NYBAKKEN Editor ROBBIN BROSTERMAN Design Director – Books

DC COMICS
DIANE NELSON President DAN DIDIO and JIM LEE Co-Publishers
GEOFF JOHNS Chief Creative Officer PATRICK CALDON EVP – Finance and Administration
JOHN ROOD EVP – Sales, Marketing and Business Development AMY GENKINS SVP – Business and Legal Affairs
STEVE ROTTERDAM SVP – Sales and Marketing JOHN CUNNINGHAM VP – Marketing
TERRI CUNNINGHAM VP – Managing Editor ALISON GILL VP – Manufacturing
DAVID HYDE VP – Publicity SUE POHJA VP – Book Trade Sales ALYSSE SOLL VP – Advertising and Custom Publishing
BOB WAYNE VP – Sales MARK CHIARELLO Art Director

GREEK STREET: CASSANDRA COMPLEX

DC Comics, 1700 Broadway, New York, NY 10019
A Warner Bros. Entertainment Company.
Printed by Quad/Graphics, Dubuque, IA, USA. 10/20/10. First printing.
ISBN: 978-1-4012-2847-7

probably shouldnt have told her.

M-MY GOD, EDDIE. YOU **DID** IT WITH YOUR OWN MOTHER. THEN YOU...

IT WAS AN ACCIDENT. I...I WAS DRUNK, INNIT. I WANTED TO...TO **FIND** HER.

oh fuck me. where did this come from.

I'D SPENT SO LONG WONDERING WHERE SHE WAS AND... YOU KNOW...**WHO** SHE WAS. THEN...

FUCK, SANDY. I-I'VE FUCKED EVERYTHING UP.

IT'S ME. WAIT UNTIL YOU SEE WHAT'S WASHED UP. THEY'RE SO INCREDIBLY **PERFECT!**

WHAT ARE WE GOING TO DO NOW? I'M FIFTEEN, **YOU'RE** WANTED FOR MURDER...

GO TO LONDON. FIND THAT COPPER I SAW AT FUREY'S CLUB.

DEDALUS

KIDS, THERE'S BEEN A SLIGHT CHANGE OF PLAN. WE HAVE TO MAKE A **TEENY** DETOUR.

"WAIT.

"LET'S STOP THERE..."

6

...LET'S GO BACK.

NO, NOT TWENTY-FIVE HUNDRED YEARS. NOT TO THOSE OLIVE-SCENTED DAYS OF AESCHYLUS AND EURIPIDES...

THOUGH YOU'D BE FORGIVEN FOR THINKING THOSE DAYS HAD NEVER QUITE ENDED...

LET US REWIND JUST A LITTLE.

A SON RETURNS EARLY FROM HOLIDAY, JUST HOURS AFTER OUR MOTHER-FUCKING HERO FLEES ILIUM.

THE SON'S NAME IS PAOLO. A YOUNG ARISTOCRAT...

"...SON OF MENON."

MOTHER, IT'S ME. ARE YOU HOME? ARE YOU SOBER?

MYKONOS WAS INSANE. SURPRISED I GOT OUT ALIVE.

SANDY?

COME ON, SIS. YOU MUST HAVE HAD A VISION THAT I WAS COMING OR SOMETHING.

SORRY. VERY BAD JOKE. I'M, LIKE, TOTALLY EVIL.

7

"...UNTIL, IT SEEMS, *NOW...*"

...A SHARP INSTRUMENT?

YOU MEAN--?

AN *AXE?* A REALLY BIG AXE.

FORGET IT, DEDALUS. THERE ARE PARTICLES OF HUMAN SKIN AND FINGERNAIL IN THE WOUND.

HUMAN?

WELL, HUMAN... BUT *NOT* HUMAN.

THE RIBCAGE?

AS YOU MIGHT HAVE NOTICED, SUCH WAS THE SAVAGERY OF THE ATTACK, MUCH OF THE SKULL WAS REMOVED.

THE RIBCAGE, HOWEVER, WAS UNTOUCHED.

NO PAGE TORN FROM MEDEA. OUR MONSTER... IS CHANGING ITS M.O.

OR...OR WAS IT *INTERRUPTED?*

I... I ONLY W-WANT TO HELP YOU.

I WAS LIKE YOU, ONCE. I--I WAS DEAD LIKE YOU.

I WAS DEAD INSIDE, SISTER.

WH... WH... WHO...

N-NO ONE ELSE KNOWS YOU'RE HERE. NOT EVEN MY SISTERS. YOU'RE SAFE HERE, YEAH?

COME ON, SISTER. TALK TO ME... TRUST ME...

WHO ARE YOU? WHAT'S YOUR NAME?

M-ME... ME...

MEE...

...MEDEA...

WHAT DID ESTHER MEAN BY THAT SUICIDE LETTER?

MY DAUGHTER HAS BEEN ABDUCTED. MY WIFE DRIVEN TO SUICIDE. I NEED TO FIND THE MAN RESPONSIBLE.

WHAT ABOUT THE POLICE?

WHY HIPPOLYTUS?

OH, THEY'LL DO THEIR BEST. WHICH, AS USUAL, WON'T BE NEARLY GOOD ENOUGH.

BESIDES, I'D LIKE TO DEAL WITH THE BASTARD MYSELF.

HEAR THAT, BRO? THE LORD MUST BE SPENDING TOO MUCH TIME WITH US LOT.

FUCK THE LAW. HE WANTS TO DO THINGS THE OLD WAY.

ALL I KNOW IS, HIS NAME IS EDDIE. AND IF MY WIFE TOOK HIM HOME, HE'S LIKELY TO BE YOUNG. WINSOME.

AND VERY PROBABLY STUPID.

OH GOD, I CAN HEAR THEM.

ALL RIGHT, MENON. BUT NOTHING'S FOR FREE.

ARGH!

UNG!

JUST TELL THE STORY, GIRL.

BRING THE AUDIENCE UP TO DATE...WITH THIS SIMPLE TALE OF LOVE AND LOSS...

AND FORGET ALL THESE CRAZY IDEAS ABOUT GETTING INVOLVED.

SHIT, WHY AM I SO FUCKED UP BY THE IDEA OF EDDIE AND THAT YOUNG GIRL... IN THE HANDS OF THOSE MONSTERS... ANYWAY?

IS IT BECAUSE SHE'S JUST FIFTEEN? LIKE I WAS, WHEN I FELL FOR MY MONSTER, BACK IN KENSAL RISE...

WHAT'S UP, CHANTEL?

SORRY, OWEN. FEEL A BIT...SICK.

SORT YOURSELF OUT. YOU'RE WANDERING AROUND LIKE A FART IN A COMA.

THANKS FOR YOUR CONCERN, YOU PRICK.

GET BACK HERE!

PISS OFF!

IF YOU'RE BORED UP THERE, WE CAN ALWAYS GET YOU WORK ON THE STREET.

LEAVE THE POOR GIRL ALONE, OWEN.

GENE? WHAT'RE YOU DOING DOWN HERE, BRO?

WHAT D'YOU THINK? LOOKING AT THE *GIRLS*.

IF YOU WANT A BIT OF ACTION, WE'LL FIX YOU UP WITH SOMETHING TASTY.

BUT YOU KNOW YOU CAN'T SMOKE HERE. YOU'LL GET US SHUT DOWN, MATE.

WE SELL DRUGS. WE SELL *BODIES*!

GENE, SHUT UP.

WE FUCKING *KILL* ANYONE WHO GETS IN OUR WAY--

YOU'RE BLADDERED. COME ON.

THIS AIN'T ABOUT SMOKING, IS IT? YOU'RE WORRIED MY FACE WILL SCARE OFF THE PUNTERS.

STAFF ONLY

--BUT WE *PISS OUR PANTS* AT THE *SMOKING BAN!* OH MY GOD! THE FEARSOME FUREYS!

THAT'S BOLLOCKS.

IT'S WHAT *FRANCIE* SAID.

FRANCIE'S A WANKER.

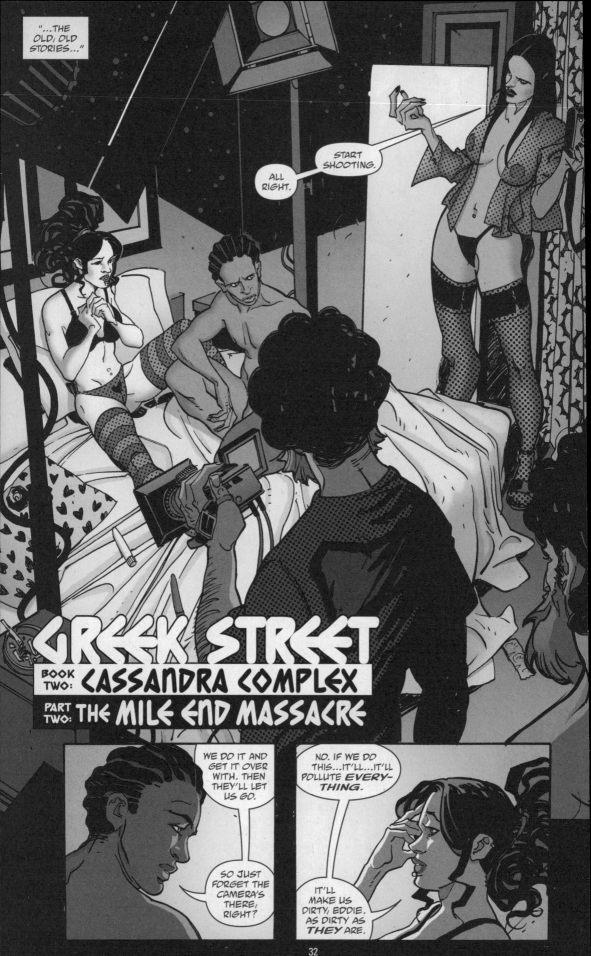

"...THE OLD, OLD STORIES..."

START SHOOTING.

ALL RIGHT.

GREEK STREET

BOOK TWO: CASSANDRA COMPLEX

PART TWO: THE MILE END MASSACRE

WE DO IT AND GET IT OVER WITH. THEN THEY'LL LET US GO.

SO JUST FORGET THE CAMERA'S THERE, RIGHT?

NO. IF WE DO THIS...IT'LL...IT'LL POLLUTE *EVERY-THING.*

IT'LL MAKE US DIRTY, EDDIE. AS DIRTY AS *THEY* ARE.

IF YOU'RE NOT GOING TO PERFORM, WE'LL GET A **PROFESSIONAL** ON HER.

OI!

LL
RS,
LY.

DON'T YOU FUCKING TOUCH HER!--

AGGH!

Y-YOUR **CHILD** CALLS FOR YOU...

THE SMELL OF FORMALDEHYDE! **VOMIT** RISES IN YOUR THROAT!

35

...YOU THINK I DID IT FOR FUCKING *FUN?*

AS GOD IS MY WITNESS, I'D RATHER *CUT MY OWN EYES OUT* THAN HURT THAT BOY.

BUT THAT WOULDN'T HAVE BEEN ENOUGH FOR *LIMM. HIS* BOY GOT CUT UP. SO *GENE* HAD TO GET DONE TOO.

SINCE WHEN DO THE *FUREYS* TAKE THEIR ORDERS FROM THOSE CHINESE *FUCKERS?*

WE CAN'T AFFORD A WAR. NOT WITH THAT CROWD.

HE WOULDN'T HAVE BEEN PUSHED AROUND LIKE THAT, WOULD HE?

HE WOULD HAVE TOLD LIMM TO GO *FUCK* HIMSELF.

JESUS, AIN'T YOU ALWAYS TELLING US HOW HE KICKED *BILLY HILL'S* ARSE?

M-MAYBE HE **WOULD** HAVE STOOD UP TO LIMM. BUT I AIN'T HIM. I AIN'T YOUR GRANDDAD.

YOU'RE JUST A FRIGHTENED LITTLE MAN.

YOU'RE RIGHT THERE. HE WAS A FUCKING **GOD**.

OWEN, DON'T DO ANYTHING SILLY...

YOU **TRIED** TO MAKE ME BE LIKE YOU, DIDN'T YOU? THE GREAT TAN FUREY.

EVERY DAY...EVERY DAY YOU'D LAY INTO ME.

LOOK. YOU MADE A RIGHT FUCKING MEAL OUT OF ME. B-BUT IT DIDN'T WORK. I AIN'T LIKE YOU.

YOU WOULDN'T BE WORRIED ABOUT WHAT YOUR SONS WERE GOING TO GET UP TO.

WHEREAS ME...

"...I'M BRICKING IT."

MILE END ROAD E3
STERI IE
C ROI

RED DRAGON
CHINESE RESTAURANT

WHO'S *THAT?*

HE'LL DO.

GENE, YOU SURE YOU'RE UP FOR THIS?

I'M THE ONE WITH THE FACE LIKE AN ABORTION, AIN'T I?

GOOD BOY.

MASKS ON, CHAPS.

LET'S REALLY GIVE 'EM A PERFORMANCE.

"NOT ABSOLUTELY
SURE WHY WE'RE
HERE, SIR..."

I MEAN, ALL RIGHT. THIS IS TERRIBLE...

FOUR INNOCENTS DEAD. MANY MORE WOUNDED. AN APPARENTLY SENSELESS MASSACRE.

BUT WHAT'S IT GOT TO DO WITH THE *GREEK STREET MURDERS?*

WHAT'S IT GOT TO DO WITH THE SUICIDE OF *LADY ESTHER?*

AN INTRIGUING SUICIDE LETTER ABOUT THE RAPE THAT MIGHT *NOT* HAVE BEEN A RAPE?

I DON'T KNOW, RASHID.

I DON'T KNOW HOW IT ALL FITS TOGETHER.

AND I DON'T KNOW WHY WE'RE *HERE.*

A STRANGE WOMAN RECENTLY TO ME I WAS IN *LABYRINT* THAT'S HOW FEEL.

LOST IN THE MIDDLE O SOME KIND O LABYRINTH.

MAYBE I HOPE THAT IF I KEEP BLUNDERING AROUND I CAN... I CAN...

AVOID THE *MINOTAUR,* SIR?

FIND THE EXIT.

...HE'S A DETECTIVE OR SOMETHING...

NAH, SOMEONE ELSE WON'T DO. I ONLY WANT TO SPEAK TO DEDALUS.

bollocks. i'll try later then.

i nicked some money from this prick in a petrol station a few miles back.

he wore a suit and drove a beemer so am i guilty?

i feel light-headed now. almost flying.

need to eat something, man.

sandy? said she'd meet me here with the tea and chocolate.

she wouldn't have run off with the money. she aint like that

THE TIMES
WIFE OF LORD MENON DEAD
Suicide Letter
Found

44

SANDY!

COME BACK, BABE!

N-NO. I'VE GOT TO GO HOME. MUMMY'S DEAD!

MY POOR BROTHER FOUND HER. I HAVE TO GO TO PAOLO. MAKE SURE HE'S ALL RIGHT.

YOU GO BACK THERE AND WE'LL NEVER BE TOGETHER AGAIN.

WH-WHY DID SHE DO IT? WHY DID SHE KILL HERSELF?

I...I THINK THAT MIGHT HAVE HAD SOMETHING TO DO WITH ME.

YOU? NO, IT WAS SOMETHING ELSE...

I KNOW. LOOK, I'M WELL SORRY. I KNOW IT HURTS AND THAT...

SH-SHE COULD BE A PAIN A-AND A DRUNK...BUT...

SHE WAS THERE FOR ME...WHEN I HAD MY ACCIDENT.

"THE SUICIDE NOTE..."

...LADY ESTHER CLAIMED TO HAVE BEEN RAPED. BUT SHE PUT A QUOTE IN IT...

"OH MISERABLE DOOM OF UNHAPPY WOMEN."

WELL REMEMBERED, SIR. WE'LL MAKE A CLASSICIST OUT OF YOU YET...

ANYWAY, SHE KNEW HER HUSBAND WOULD RECOGNIZE THE QUOTE AND INFER THAT SHE HADN'T IN FACT BEEN RAPED.

SO SOMETHING ELSE MADE HER COMMIT SUICIDE.

SOMETHING, OR SOMEONE.

INDEED.

READY FOR YOUR DESCENT INTO HADES?

NICE-LOOKING GIRL.

NOT REALLY MY TYPE.

this is it

right now

ALL RIGHT, GENE. **DO** THE LITTLE PRICK.

now ive lost everything else

GO AHEAD. **KILL** ME. I DON'T GIVE A **FUCK.**

everything --

WH...WHA--?

EDDIE? WHAT HAPPENED? DID YOU SEE SOME-THING?

TH-THEY... THE FUREYS... THEY'RE GOING TO...

I DIDN'T SEE A THIN WHY DIDN'T SEE MY OV VISION?

MAYBE IT'S AN *ORACLE*. THERE'S A LOT OF IT ABOUT NOWADAYS.

DIDN'T C-CARE...ABOUT DYING. LOST EVERYTHING...

WH-WHAT... DOES THAT MEAN?

WE SHOULD GO. YOU TOO, SANDY.

HOW DO YOU KNOW MY NAME? WHO... *ARE* YOU?

ME? I'M NOBODY.

I'M JUST A DANCER. PROBLEM, EDDIE?

DEDALUS.

YES, I'VE SEEN HIM...HE'S PART OF THE STORY...

Y-YEAH. WE GOT TO GET TO LONDON. TALK TO THIS COP. HE'S CALLED... *DEDALUS.* HE MIGHT BE ABLE TO HELP US.

MAYBE SHE'S ESCAPED FROM SOMEWHERE...

YOU KNOW, SOME KIND OF HOSPITAL. MAYBE SHE'S HAD AN ACCIDENT. OR...

OR...?

OR...SHE'S THE RESULT OF SOME KIND OF FREAKISH SCIENTIFIC EXPERIMENT.

HMM. TRY TO KEEP A LID ON THAT IMAGINATION OF YOURS, RASHID.

I MEAN... SHE WAS DEFINITELY HUMAN, RIGHT?

LOOKED AS THOUGH SHE WAS HUMAN ONCE, SIR.

DID YOU HEAR WHAT THE WOMAN CALLED HER? MEDEA.

...ARGUABLY THE BLOODIEST WOMAN...IN ALL TRAGEDY...

YOU'RE FAMILIAR WITH MEDEA?

LORD MENON TOLD ME ABOUT HER. TRIED TO GET THROUGH THE PLAY MYSELF. SCARY STUFF.

BUT I DON'T REALLY SEE...WHAT THAT'S GOT TO DO WITH ANYTHING...

58

...ORD.

...ME IN. ...USE THE ...ESS.

MESS, KILLIS? IT'S POSITIVELY *ANTISEPTIC.*

I SUPPOSE YOU WANT A PROGRESS REPORT. I MUST SAY, YOU'VE GOT YOURSELF TANGLED UP IN SOME VERY--

NO, KILLIS.

ACTUALLY, THERE'S BEEN A *CHANGE* IN MY PRIORITIES.

MY DAUGHTER...

YES, I KNOW ALL ABOUT YOUR DAUGHTER.

A NICE, NORMAL, UPPER-CLASS *GEL*... UNTIL THE AGE OF ELEVEN.

THAT'S WHEN THINGS START TO GO WRONG. SHE'S HARDLY SEEN OUT OF THE HOUSE. THERE ARE DARK RUMORS...

A DOCTOR'S REPORT.

THE POSSIBILITY OF *SEXUAL ABUSE*--

SHUT YOUR BLOODY MOUTH!

IF YOU DON'T GET YOUR HANDS OFF OF ME...I'LL SNAP YOUR TRACHEA AND WATCH YOU CHOKE TO DEATH.

LORD... OR NO LORD.

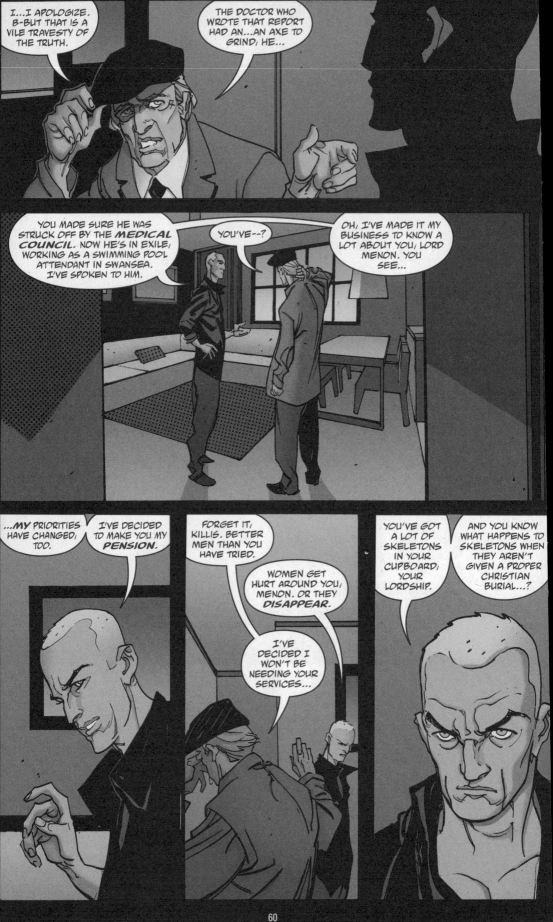

A DEAD BODY, SERENA...

YOU WERE ONE OF THREE WOMEN WHO RAIDED A GOVERNMENT BUILDING AND TOOK A DEAD BODY.

DO YOU KNOW HOW SERIOUS AN OFFENSE THAT IS?

WHY DID YOU STEAL A DEAD BODY? WHO IS THAT PERSON...OR THING THAT I SAW TODAY?

YOU CALLED HER MEDEA. PAGES OF THE PLAY, MEDEA, WERE FOUND IN EACH VICTIM'S CHEST CAVITY.

I THINK THE PERSON YOU CALL MEDEA IS RESPONSIBLE FOR A NUMBER OF MURDERS IN LONDON. AND I THINK YOU'RE EITHER HELPING OR PROTECTING HER.

I'VE GOT ENOUGH TO CHARGE YOU WITH, SERENA.

WAS MEDEA ONCE A **DEAD WOMAN?**

WAS SHE ONCE A DEAD WOMAN? WHAT KIND OF A QUESTION IS THAT?

ANY BETTER IDEAS?

YOU MUST HAVE WATCHED ENOUGH WILDLIFE PROGRAMS. HAVE YOU EVER SEEN ANYTHING REMOTELY LIKE THAT THING?

PEOPLE DO NOT COME BACK FROM THE DEAD. THAT'S IMPOSSIBLE.

WHEN I WAS A LITTLE GIRL...THE CHANCES OF ME ENDING UP IN A JOB LIKE *THIS* SEEMED PRETTY IMPOSSIBLE.

SIR.

london.

HERE?

WE GET OUT HERE?

big place, london.

I'M SORRY, B I'VE GOT YO AWAY FROM T PORNOGRAPHE I'VE DONE THE RIGHT THING.

GOOD LUCK, KID WE'RE A GONNA NEED I

RIGHT

62

--GGH!

YOU TELL YOUR BOSS THAT, FUCKER.

TAN FUREY MIGHT BE IN HIS GRAVE...

...BUT HE CAN STILL FUCK HIM UP.

MY OLD GRANDDAD...HE RULED THIS PART OF THE WORLD. HE'S DEAD...BUT HE CAN STILL REACH OUT...

THROUGH ME...

AEEIGHH!

EDDIE, I'M REALLY... SCARED.

I'M THE ONE WHO SAW HIS OWN DEATH.

BUT MY VISIONS... TH-THEY'RE... CHANGING.

MAYBE IF YOU TALKED ABOUT--

I CAN'T TALK ABOUT IT! DON'T... REMEMBER...

I...I...

TRY. COME ON, THERE MUST BE SOMETHING.

I...I REMEMBER... WHEN I STARTED GOING STRANGE... THE DOCTORS. TOO MANY DOCTORS...

THEY DIDN'T BELIEVE ME...WHEN I TOLD THEM...

WHEN YOU TOLD THEM WHAT?

SANDY... WHAT DID YOU TELL THE DOCTORS?

"FUCKING NERVE OF THE BASTARDS."

THEY COULD HAVE WAITED UNTIL WE'D FINISHED OUR DINNER, AT LEAST.

WELL, YOU DID TORCH ONE OF THEIR PLACES, GENE.

Y-YEAH. YEAH, I SUPPOSE WE DID.

WHERE THE FUCK IS THIS GONNA END, DAD?

GET SOME REST, SON. WE'LL SORT IT OUT.

OH, CHANTEL. YOU'RE BACK.

GENE, YOU REMEMBER THAT COPPER?

"DEDALUS..."

WHAT'S SHE DOING?

DOING, SIR?

...I BELIEVE IT'S CALLED *LEVITATION*.

AT A PUSH...SHE CAN SUMMON DIONYSUS. LORD OF THE IRRATIONAL...

DIONYSUS--?

VERY DANGEROUS CHARACTER, SIR.

SERENA...? THIS IS... THIS IS VERY IMPRESSIVE BUT...

YOU'RE LOOKING FOR SERENA?

70

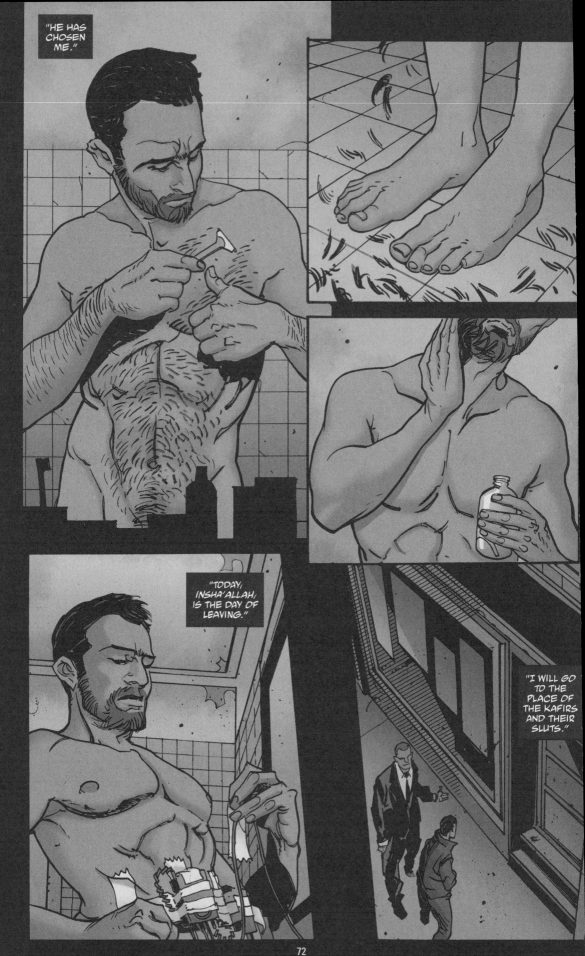

"HE HAS CHOSEN ME."

"TODAY, INSHA'ALLAH, IS THE DAY OF LEAVING."

"I WILL GO TO THE PLACE OF THE KAFIRS AND THEIR SLUTS."

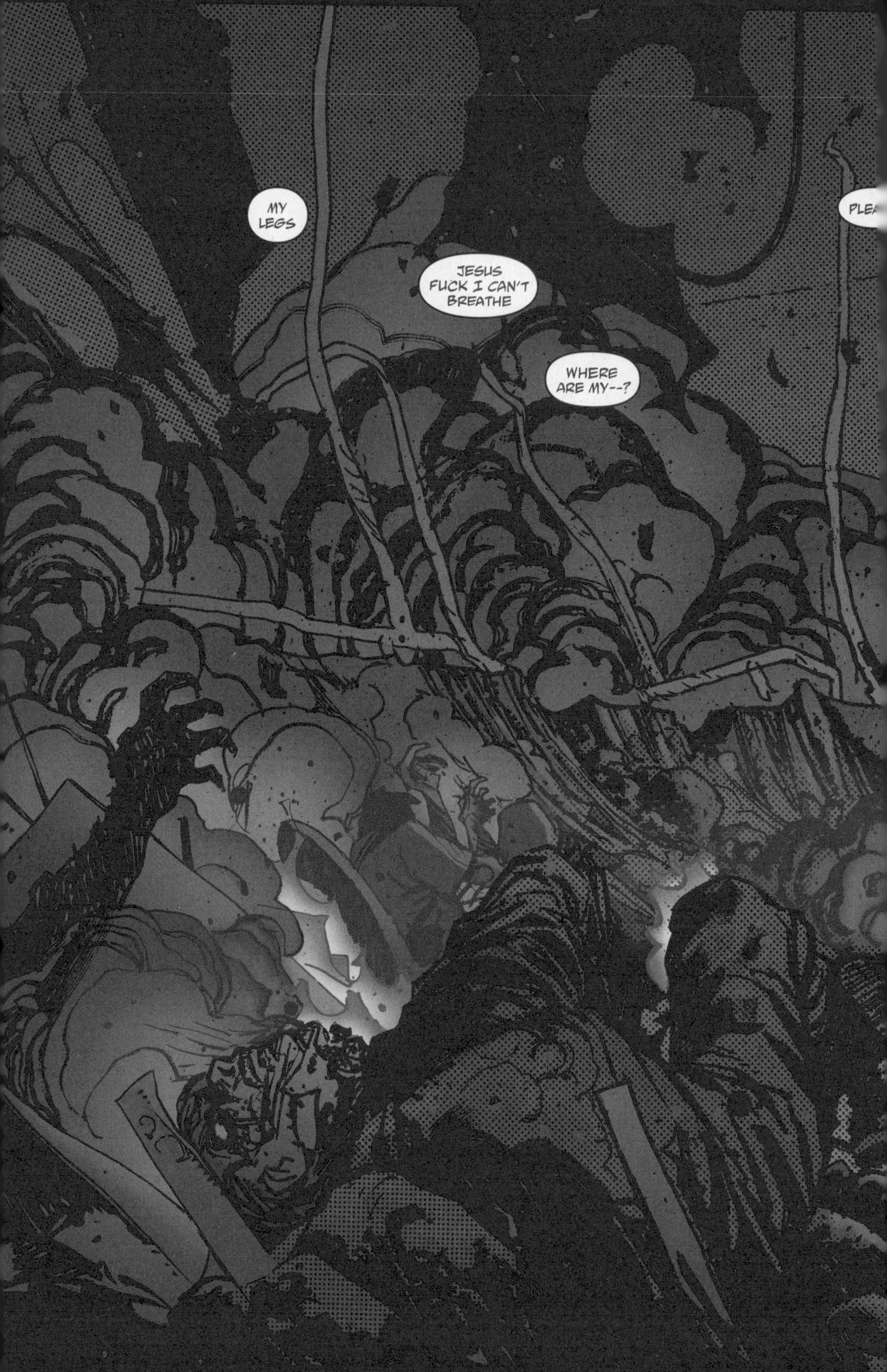
MY LEGS
JESUS FUCK I CAN'T BREATHE
WHERE ARE MY--?
PLEA

OH MY GOD OH MY GOD
HELP ME, PLEASE
I STILL CAN'T
"I CAN'T LOOK AT THIS ANY LONGER..."
GREEK STREET
BOOK TWO:
CASSANDRA COMPLEX
PART FOUR:
THE HOUSE OF PAIN
"SEND MADNESS ON THIS MAN, CONFOUND HIS MIND..."
EURIPEDES, HERAKLES

80

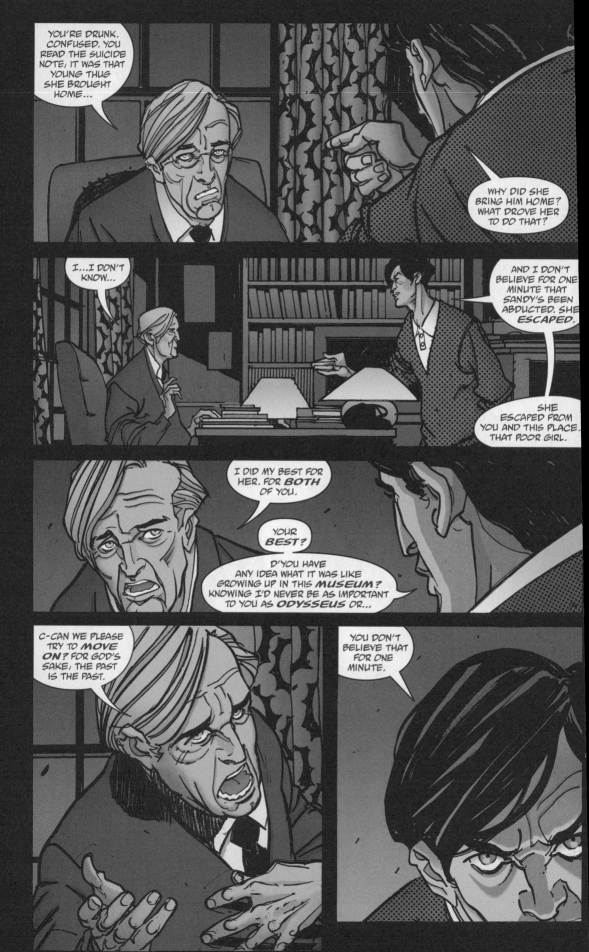

"YOU **KNOW** THE PAST IS RIGHT HERE WITH US..."

MY FATHER? WH-WHAT'S MY FATHER GOT TO DO WITH THIS?

I DON'T UNDER-STAND...

I'M GUESSING, MAN. YOU'RE ALWAYS GOING ON ABOUT WHAT A BASTARD HE IS.

SOMETHING BAD HAPPENED TO YOU, SANDY? SOMETHING THE DOCTORS WOULDN'T BELIEVE. SOMETHING THAT, LIKE, **SHOCKED** YOU INTO BEING THE WAY YOU--

SLAPP

HOW DARE YOU!

Y-YOU DON'T KNOW THE FIRST THING ABOUT ME. **OR** MY FATHER.

THAT AIN'T TRUE, BABES.

ANYONE HOME?

CHANTEL?

MAYBE
SHOULD
OUTSIDE,
RASHID.

I'LL STAY HERE IF THAT'S ALL RIGHT, SIR.

SO WHAT NOW? ARE WE A TARGET FOR AL QAEDA?

IT WAS PROBABLY A ONE-OFF.

THE THING IS, THERE'S NO NEED FOR YOU TO GO ON TAKING IT OUT ON THE CHINESE.

I'VE BEEN IN TOUCH WITH OLD MAN LIMM. HE'S WILLING TO MEET YOU, HAROLD. TRY TO SORT OUT THIS...

HOLD ON.

BRR BRR

DEDALUS.

FIRST THING, I DIDN'T MEAN TO KILL NO ONE.

WHO IS THIS?

THE PAPERS CALLED ME... THE TOY BOY KILLER.

PRETTY BOY.

I USED TO GET PISSED OFF WHEN THEY CALLED ME THAT. PROBLEM SORTED, EH?

AH, GENE. BABY. I...I DID IT...TO STOP A WAR...

AND NOW WE'VE GOT ONE ANYWAY. DON'T MAKE ME LAUGH, DAD. IT'LL MAKE MY STITCHES POP.

M-MY DAD... YOUR GRANDFATHER... HE USED TO KNOCK THE SHIT OUT OF ME. THE SKIN WOULD BE...HANGING OFF...

HE SAW IT IN ME, SEE. HE SAW IT...

MAYBE WE'RE CURSED. THE HOUSE OF FUREY. THE HOUSE OF PAIN...

DAD, WE'D BETTER GET READY IF--

JESUS, ARE YOU ALL RIGHT?

HE SAW IT...

89

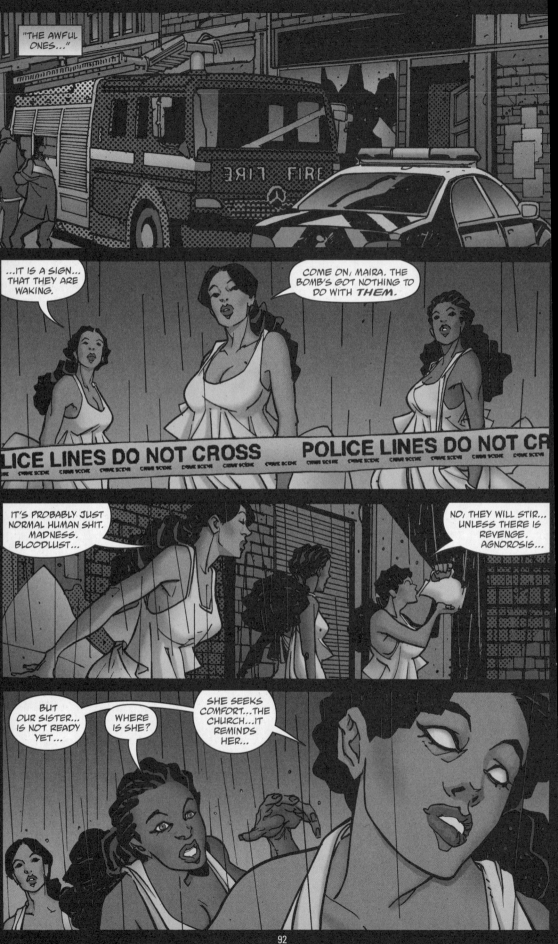

...OH, IT SOUNDS R..."

SOMEONE'S GOING IN.

WAIT HERE. IF I NEED YOU, I'LL WHISTLE.

CAREFUL, SIR. HE'S WANTED FOR MURDER. HE COULD BE DANGEROUS.

AH, HE DIDN'T *SOUND* DANGEROUS.

HE JUST SOUNDED LIKE A SCARED KID.

ANYONE HERE?

EDDIE?

EDDIE...IT'S A CHURCH...

THIS IS WHERE HE WANTED TO MEET.

BUT MY VISION...MY *BAD* VISION... ICONS WEEPING BLOOD, IT WAS...

WAS *I* IN YOUR VISION?

N-NO...

THEN THIS AIN'T YOUR VISION.

WE'RE JUST GOING TO EXPLAIN TO THE NICE POLICEMAN THAT I'M INNOCENT AND THEN GO HOME.

IF YOU'RE GOOD I'LL EVEN MAKE YOU A CUP OF TEA.

"SEEMS THE MORE WE FEAR...

"MOST OF IT'S SHIT, OF COURSE, BUT MAYBE THERE ARE THOSE WHO REALLY HAVE A GIFT.

"THOSE WHO CARRY ON THE SPIRIT OF APOLLO'S PRIESTESS.

"TAKE SANDY, DAUGHTER OF LORD MENON. HER CRAZED GAZE SEEMED TO CUT THROUGH TIME ITSELF."

"BUT HER BIG VISION. DEDALUS DYING IN A CHURCH. WELL..."

GREEK STREET

BOOK TWO:
CASSANDRA COMPLEX

PART FIVE:
ORACLE

103

...THAT *ZEUS.* THAT ANIMAL...

THAT WICKED SWAN. THAT *DESTROYER.*

COME, *SISTER.* COME! WE HAVE HIM FOR YOU!

WE'RE CALLING TO YOU.

MEDEA...

NOTEBOOK OF LORD MENON OF ILIUM. MAYFAIR, LONDON.

BEFORE NOW, I NEVER TOOK MUCH NOTICE OF MY DAUGHTER'S RAVINGS. THE POOR CHILD'S BEEN THROUGH SO MUCH. SO VERY MUCH.

THOUGH MY HEAD MIGHT BE FIRMLY STUCK FOR MUCH OF THE TIME IN THE ANCIENT WORLD, I AM NONETHELESS A MODERN.

AS SUCH I CANNOT BELIEVE IN ORACLES. PROPHECIES. RATIONALLY, THEY MAKE NO SENSE.

BUT I HAVE FELT FOR SOME TIME THAT I AM NO LONGER COMPLETELY IN THE WORLD OF THE RATIONAL.

BZZZZZZZ
BZZZZZZZ

I SUPPOSE YOU'D BETTER COME IN.

KILLIS.

HELLO, WHAT'S THIS, THEN? GIRL-FRIEND OF YOURS?

WHAT ARE YOU DOING HERE, KILLIS?

your gone now. i never want to see you again.

You abandoned me. now i abandon you.

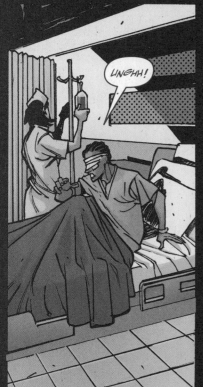

UNGHH!

I...I CAN'T SEE NOTHING...

YOU HAVE TO LEAVE THOSE ON, EDDIE. UNTIL WE FIND OUT WHAT YOU'VE DONE TO YOURSELF.

i abandon you.

115

"DEDALUS, JUST MAKING SURE YOU REMEMBERED OUR LAST CONVERSATION..."

"I REMEMBER IT. BUT I'M NOT GOING TO BE BLACKMAILED BY PEOPLE LIKE YOU, FUREY..."

"...THE LIES YOU TOLD, THE LABYRINTH OF FALSEHOODS ...YOU'RE A CRAFTSMAN, THE WAY YOU'VE CONSTRUCTED YOUR COUNTERFEIT LIFE..."

GREEK STREET

BOOK TWO: CASSANDRA COMPLEX

PART SIX: AGNOROSIS

WHAT IS THE RITE OF PURIFICATION? HOW BEST SHALL IT BE DONE?
—SOPHOCLES OEDIPUS THE KING.

"DO THE KID, OR IT ALL GETS TORN DOWN..."

"I REPEAT..

...THE BOY IS IMPURE.

THERE IS A RITE FOR THAT.

WE SHOULD HELP OUR SISTER TRY AGAIN.

SHE IS UNABLE TO RIGHT THE BALANCE. WHEN SHE IMAGINES A MAN TO BE HER DESTROYER, SHE CAN BECOME AVENGING *MEDEA*.

BUT WHEN SHE MEETS THE *REAL THING*...

Medea

UGGNN!

WH-WHA--?

I'M BLIND, RIGHT? IN ONE EYE?

TOO EARLY TO KNOW. THERE ARE PROCEDURES WE CAN TRY...BUT YOUR EYE WILL HAVE TO SETTLE DOWN FIRST.

LOOK, MAN. THERE'S THIS GIRL. SHE WAS HURT. HER NAME'S SANDY.

SANDY. RIGHT. I'LL SEE WHAT I CAN FIND OUT.

STAY THERE, A NURSE WILL TAKE YOU BACK TO YOUR BED.

nurse?

the way i was brought up i know when people are bullshitting.

doctors. coppers. council workers, all of them. all the same.

fucking bullshitting bastards.

PUT THESE ON, EDDIE. WE'RE GOING FOR A DRIVE.

NICE PATCH, BY THE WAY. VERY *PIRATES OF THE CARIBBEAN.*

BASTARDS!

LINGH!

well, you try shutting one eye and sprinting out a door.

this is my so-called mother's fault.

her fault for having me.

her fault for not wanting me.

YOU'RE GOING TO HAVE TO TELL US WHAT YOU'VE BEEN UP TO WITH EDDIE, SANDY. IT'S IMPORTANT.

WHERE IS HE? I WANT TO SEE HIM.

HE'S BEING TAKEN SOMEWHERE FOR HIS OWN SAFETY.

I KNOW WHAT THAT MEANS! *PRISON.* EDDIE DOESN'T DESERVE THAT. HE'S HAD PRISON ALL HIS LIFE.

LORD MENON, I...I DIDN'T KNOW YOU WERE HERE.

I'D LIKE TO TAKE MY DAUGHTER HOME. THE CONSULTANT TELLS ME THERE ARE NO MEDICAL REASONS TO KEEP HER IN.

SANDY IS HELPING US WITH SOME QUESTIONS.

RIGHT.

I SPOKE TO YOUR *CHIEF COMMISSIONER,* WHO IS A PERSONAL FRIEND. HE ASSURES ME THERE'LL BE NO PROBLEM.

I HAVE GIVEN UP WONDERING HOW A DEAD WOMAN CAN RETURN.

Ilium

JUST AS I GAVE UP WONDERING WHAT HAPPENED TO ALL THE GIRLS I DISCARDED. ESTHER WAS RIGHT ABOUT THIS POOR THING. ANOTHER OF MY OLD FLAMES.

IF MY MEMORY IS CORRECT SHE ALSO GOT PREGNANT, LIKE MISCHA. BUT THIS ONE WAS BALLSY. PROUD. SHE DIDN'T WANT MY HELP. DISAPPEARED.

PAOLO, HOW IS SHE?

SLEEPING, FINALLY. SHE'S EXHAUSTED.

YOU LOOK PRETTY GHASTLY YOURSELF. ARE YOU SURE YOU DON'T WANT ME TO STAY?

NO, YOU GO OUT AND ENJOY YOURSELF.

I'M JUST A LITTLE TIRED. IT'S BEEN A LONG DAY.

THERE'S NO MENTION OF CHILDREN IN THE NEWS REPORT. WHAT HAPPENED TO HER? ABORTION, PERHAPS?

KRSKK

i knew what was happening. i knew she was kissing me, undressing me. i wanted it.

i wasn't so drunk i didn't know i was fucking my own mother.

it didn't feel bad. it didn't feel wrong.

in the morning i pretended to be shocked. pretended to be disgusted.

that's what feels wrong.

GREEK STREET W1

END OF BOOK TWO. TO BE CONTINUED IN GREEK STREET: AJAX

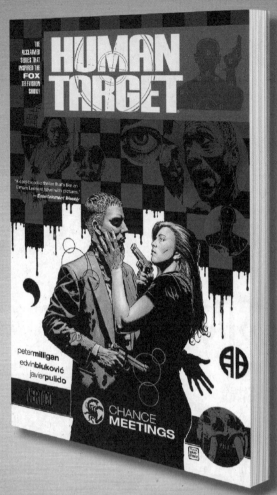
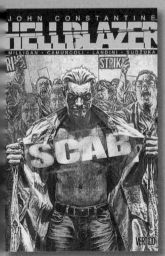

DECEPTION
LUST
BETRAYAL
MURDER

DONT MISS THESE OTHER TITLES FROM VERTIGO CRIME

SUGGESTED FOR MATURE READERS

THE CHILL
By JASON STARR Author of
PANIC ATTACK and THE FOLLO
Art by MICK BERTILORENZI
JANUARY 20

THE BRONX KILL
By PETER MILLIGAN
Author of GREEK STREET
Art by JAMES ROMBERGER
MARCH 2010

AREA 10
By CHRISTOS N. GAGE
Art by CHRIS SAMNEE
APRIL 2010

VERTIGO CRIME
vertigocomics.com